A Trip to the Land of Funny Animals
Oral motor and myofunctional exercise for toddlers

Illustrations: Karin Berenshtein
First Edition: 2022
All rights reserved Hilit Braun

About the Book

A Trip to the Land of Funny Animals is a familiar and well-known scenario of taking a trip to the zoo, which most children are familiar with. This allows adults to expose toddlers to a variety of tongue and speech organ exercises, in a pragmatic way that integrates learning and fun.

Every encounter with an animal in this book contains a focused exercise. Alongside the focused exercises are exercises accompanied by additional assistance for situations where the toddler has a hard time completing the exercise without accessories. The accessories are temporary and serve as a kind of bridge until the exercise can be successfully completed without accessories. The child must be observed while performing the exercise using accessories in order to prevent injury, swallowing or inhaling foreign objects. When deliberating, contact a speech therapist for consultation.

Along with the tongue exercises found in this book, you'll encounter the Crocodile and the Turtle, which address other functions:

- The Turtle is an exercise in drinking using a straw. Positioning the tongue in the mouth while drinking with a straw encourages proper function and structure. Incorrect drinking models require practice and advice from a speech therapist, who should be contacted for consultation, guidance and treatment since there are other functional and structural contexts relating to proper models for drinking and swallowing.
- The Crocodile is an exercise designed to increase control over the size of the jaw opening (the exercise does not address the stability of the jaw).

The exercises and the learning in this book are based on imitation. Voluntary movements based on imitation of speech organs can be challenging for toddlers when carried out upon request. Repeated practice will advance the acquisition of oral-motor imitation skills.

Tongue and Mouth Functions for Toddlers

The muscles of the tongue, mouth and face are complex physiological structures. The improper function of these structures may affect the structure, and in turn affect the functioning as well. It is a dynamic structure operating in tandem with the physical mechanism of breathing and swallowing. As we examine the functions of the mouth, we're required to distinguish between a mouth shut during rest, standard breathing through the nose (unlike breathing through the mouth), swallowing and chewing functions, the tongue's position during rest, and the stability of the jaw, lips, cheeks and tongue. Likewise, there's great significance to the sensory component of the mouth's functions. To examine all the functions of the mouth and tongue, contact a speech therapist for diagnosis and organized treatment.

Ideas for Working with the Book

The adult reads the book to the child in a practical manner, demonstrating the exercises for the toddler and mutually imitating the exercises.

From the second reading onward, the adult reads the story while the child demonstrates the movements that the animal makes.

Animate and present the book using dolls and practical exercises during play.

Photograph and film funny faces based on characters appearing in the book.

During exercises, it's best to work in front of a mirror.

About the Author

Hilit Braun is a speech therapist with a B.A. in Communication Disorders, a B.A. in Behavioral Sciences and an M.A. in Labor Studies. She works with children, teenagers and adults in the areas of communication, language, speech and the functions of the mouth

This book is not a substitute for diagnosis and treatment by a certified speech therapist.

With much gratitude to speech therapist Ariela Sharon for her professional advice, support and great equanimity.

Good morning, girls and boys,
in a moment we'll all feel joy
when before your very eyes
we'll reveal a special surprise!

What are we doing, do you know?

Can you guess where we're about to go?

The bus is waiting, everybody line up by the door!

The Land of Funny Animals is where we're headed for!

Here's Bellybutton, a chimp so cute,

sweet as a baby holding a piece of fruit.

He tries to make us laugh with a coo and a hiss,

he flashes a smile and blows us a kiss.

Come on, kids, can you do it as well?

When he gets tired and wants trouble,

he'll start to blow a lot of bubbles!

Spitty the Llama is taking a shower,

puffing her face, oh look at that glower!

She's really quite funny and loves to play games.

Come on, kids, can you do it as well?

Pssssssst.

Who's that over there looking for a meal?

Does he want some bread? Or maybe some veal?

He swishes his tongue left and right,

Hoping for something tasty to bite.

Come on, kids, can you do it as well?
There might be something yummy for you to claim
to strengthen his tongue he uses a stick –
shoves it right in, now there's a real trick.

Shorty the Giraffe is lovely and tall,

and look, her neck is oh so very long!

She stands there so comfy, like nothing is wrong.

When a butterfly suddenly lands on her snout,

she looks so confused, with a bit of a pout.

It tickles the giraffe, so she sticks out her tongue,

and up goes the butterfly like a balloon being flung!

She had a tough time so she used a stick,

but then it vanished so very quick!

Hey, who's that peeking over that bush?

They want to catch flies; do they need a push?

Golden flies and diamond flies, catching them takes improving.

They stick out their tongues really far without moving!

We made it five seconds and caught a fly made of gold.

After 10 we caught diamonds, it never gets old.

What kind of flies can you catch?

Hello there, Rocky my sweet!

How funny that the Land of Funny Animals is where we meet!

Rocky's feeling especially pleased,

a bit of water and his thirst will be eased.

He licks his lips and licks some more

and follows us all the way to the shore.

But something funny happened at that place,
Rocky got something sticky stuck on his face!
He kept on licking his face with a grin,
and we all kept on adventuring.

And who did we meet there swimming along?
The happy sushi fish, gleeful and strong.
His big mouth opens and closes real fast,
is he eating a burger? He's having a blast!

Talking to his friends, he tells them a tale
of a long and cute creature with dinosaur scales.
Who is that, kids, about to show?
Who's that coming, does anyone know?

It's Crocodile Johnny, oh, what a surprise!
He opens his mouth just a bit, despite his size.
But when a big tasty meal comes along,
his mouth opens wide like a great big yawn
and poof, just like that, the fish is gone.

Note : the purpose of this exercise is to practice control over opening the mouth. The child must be taught to gradually open in the following manner: closed mouth, slightly open mouth, slightly more open mouth, and mouth open wide.

Turbo the Turtle's mouth is really petite,

please teach him the proper way to eat.

Put the edge of the straw just inside your lips

and the slippery tongue stays back, even the tip.

It doesn't touch the straw, not even a wink,

that's how humans, turtles and even giraffes drink!

That's it, we're tired, let's go home, we're ready.

Come back tomorrow, kids – the animals miss you already!

17708887R00017